Samson
The Loopy
Junior School Hero

Dear Headmaster,

I wish to complain about one of your students.

Kerry Presswood is her name and she kissed me again today.

I said, 'Don't do that,' but she took no notice.

She keeps on saying, 'I love you, Benny Benson,' and doing it. You'd think she would be able to control herself being nine now. Once she did it in class and Simon Snoddles saw it and made a noise like an elephant's bum.

Please help me about Kerry Presswood.

Soon she'll be trying to marry me, and I've got no defence against her because she is twice my size and as fat as a dinosaur.

Yours,

Benny Benson

Kerry Dinosaur

Also available in Lions

My Teacher is an Alien *Bruce Coville*
The Fantora Family Files *Adele Geras*
Anastasia Krupnik *Lois Lowry*
Anastasia at Your Service *Lois Lowry*
We Hate Ballet *Jahnna N Malcolm*
The Millpond Ghost and Other Stories
Pamela Oldfield
A Date Can Be Deadly *Colin Pearce*
The Deadman Tapes *Michael Rosen*
Digital Vampires *Laurence Staig*
Negative Image *Andrew Taylor*

Samson Superslug

The Loopy Letters of a Junior School Hero

Ken Adams

Illustrated by Susan Hellard

Lions
An Imprint of HarperCollins*Publishers*

Dedicayshon

I dedicates this book to my editer, wot corrected my spelling. Without her I wood not be so famuss being as I am not educatid. My editer is educatid becos she speeks reel posh and don't drink her tea from a sorcer like wot I dus. A bit like the Cween, ain't she?

First published in Great Britain in Lions in 1993
1 3 5 7 9 10 8 6 4 2
Lions is an imprint of HarperCollins Children's Books,
a division of HarperCollins Publishers Ltd, 77-85 Fulham
Palace Road, Hammersmith, London W6 8JB

Text copyright © 1993 Ken Adams
Illustrations copyright © 1993 Susan Hellard
ISBN 0 00 674386 2

The author asserts the moral right to be identified as the author of the work.

Printed and bound in Great Britain
by HarperCollins Book Manufacturing Ltd, Glasgow

Dear Editor

I am writing this book because my sister, who is eleven, says you can make about one million pounds.

My sister keeps sending stories up and they keep sending them back. I think it's because they don't like stories about fairies and all that. No self-respecting person would want a book about fairies jumping around gardens saying, "I am your Fairy Godmother. I have come to let you go to the Ball tonight." Unless it was a football match.

I am called Superslug because when I was little I kept bringing slugs in the house – until Grandma sat on my biggest one. Then I couldn't do it any more. In fact I got told off real bad because they said that Grandma nearly had a nervous breakdown.

They called me Samson because when I was little I thought

I was strong and tried to lift up Dad's car. I was a bit brainless in those days, I suppose.

My real name is Benny Benson.

Please could you take this into account when paying my royalties? My agent is Philip Stocks.

He is my best friend.

He lives at 23, Sefton Close, Bletchley.

He says he will take half the money. That's all right as long as I can have most of it.

Yours

Benny Benson

PS I hope you can publish this because we are very poor. Mum has so many children she doesn't know what to do. And we had bread and butter pudding two times this week. If we get any more poorer Mum says I can't have my *Beano* any more. And Dad is working his fingers to the bone (when he's not down the pub).

Notice: Nativity Play
by Blimpton Primary School

The *Nativity Play* will be held in the School
Hall on Tuesday, December 14th. If you
wish to attend would you please sign your
name and tear off the slip below and
return it to Mrs Ledger at the School
office. This will enable us to cater for
numbers attending. Tea and refreshments
will be available at reasonable cost after
the play.

Yours faithfully

B C Hutchins
Headmaster

CAST

MARY ....Wendy Snebbings
JOSEPH ....Benny Benson
WISE MEN .... John Snow
..............................FrederickLimpton
.... Philip Pryke

AN ANGEL....................Melissa Dunton
SHEPHERDS AND SHEEP...........Class 1
ALIENS/FISH UNDER THE SEA/ANIMALS
IN THE JUNGLE/COAL MINERS..............
.. ..Class 2 and 3
TARZAN............Anthony Posslethwaite
INN KEEPER.................Jennifer Stowe
A COW IN THE STABLE....Muriel Parks
PIANIST............................Miss Purdy
CHOIR............................Class 1, 2 & 3
PRODUCER.................Mr B C Hutchins
WRITER.......................Mr B C Hutchins

We shall/shall not* be able to attend the
Nativity Play on Tuesday, December 14th.

Signed.................
Please return this form to Mrs Ledger,
School Office.

*delete as applicable

8

Dear Teacher

Please can you leave me out of the school play☐ I'm fed up of being Joseph.

First, Wendy Snebbings, who plays Mary, is too bossy. Just because I said, "Here is the baby Jesus," before we found room at the Inn is no reason to say I'm a brainless twit. I bet Mary never said that to Joseph in real life. Someone should make her show some respect.

Anyway, I'm fed up of her keep calling me Jophes, instead of Joseph. And when I don't answer when she says Jophes she calls me a brainless twit again.

Also, I'm fed up of the baby Jesus's head falling off. When I hold up the baby Jesus and say, "Hail to thee, baby Jesus!" the flippin' head falls off and rolls under the stage. Then all the stupid kids fall around laughing and having hysterics. I got to go under the stage to get the baby Jesus head because no one wants to go because of the spiders. And it takes years to find it.

And Philip Pryke, who's a King, can't say frankincense proper. We got to wait while he says dumb thinks like frankispens and frankipins and frankispen. And once we had to wait so long that one of the shepherds fell off the stage.

But the worst thing, what is excruciating boring, is waiting around while Mary tries to sing baby Jesus to sleep. Seems to me she's more likely to fright the poor child to death. In fact, if I was baby Jesus and Wendy Snebbings tried to sing me to sleep, I'd probably be kept awake for at least one hundred years.

So I prefer just to be not in the play.

Yours

Benny Benson (Class 2)

BLIMPTON'S NATIVITY PLAY IS A GREAT SUCCESS

Yesterday's play in Blimpton Primary School Hall was a resounding success with parents. Most of the school took part, and Mr B C Hutchins, the Headmaster, said, "We all worked hard to make this a successful event."

There were, however, several small mishaps. As soon as the production started, a small child from the audience wandered down to the stage, told Joseph that he was "a pigface", and tried to shoot him with his water pistol. In the play itself, one of the Wise Men from the East suddenly burst into tears while trying to say Frankincense, and in the Jungle scene, Tarzan tripped over a gorilla and fell flat on his face.

The production also took the novel step of organising scenes where aliens from Outer Space came to earth and asked in various places, "Where is the baby Jesus?" Neither the fish under the sea nor the miners in the mines knew the answer, but eventually the jungle folk told them that he was where he'd always been, in Bethlehem.

A good time was had by all!

Mr Hutchins said I got to do the school play or I don't do no football practice.

Our School Play

So our school play were great, weren't it after all? We made a cardboard spaceship with flashing lights and all the aliens go into it while they look for baby Jesus. But the door kept sticking and my Grandma fell asleep while we were waiting. She snored so loud we thought a motorbike had come into the room.

And there was a big battle with cardboard swords, and the aliens came and said, "Where is the baby Jesus?" And everyone stopped fighting (which are really stupid, ain't it? Seems to me, no one would stop fighting a great battle just because someone said, "Where is the baby Jesus?". If they said that to me I'd chop their stupid heads off, wouldn't I?).

Anthony Posslethwaite, who was Tarzan, got told off. That's because he tripped over a gorilla and laughed. Mr Hutchins said, "Posslethwaite, this are a serious play." Seems to me it's really boring, what with girls dancing around being waves with great long bits of green toilet paper. Although when Kerry Presswood came on it was more like the sea, wasn't it, because she looked like a great blue whale dancing around.

Dear Father Christmas

I'm sorry that I couldn't put your letter up the chimney. This is because we haven't got a chimney, only central heating. So I sent the letter to your home in Lapland.

I'm not sure if I believe in you, but just in case, I wrote this letter. For Christmas I would like a motor-bike, like my big brother's got. Then I can follow spies and things like that.

My dad keeps saying that all he wants for Christmas is a win on the Pools so he won't have to go to work any more. And my mum says that she don't want him around the house all day because his socks stink up the place too much. Perhaps it's best that you don't give my dad a Christmas present.

Yours

Benny

PS My grandad says that all he wants for Christmas is his two front teeth and all the rest, because he ain't got none. P'raps you can help.

Dear Sunday School Teacher

I don't want to come on the carol singing around Milton Keynes next year.

This is because nobody wants you doing it.

I went to lots of doors and the people said, "Buzz off you, we want to be left in peace."

Also the Vicar sings too loud, like he's being slowly strangled. I got a headache just listening.

And when we went to give presents to the old people at the Old Folks Home they were ungrateful. I gave a present to a really old man and he said, "I don't want nothing. They always gives me scarves." And he threw it in the fire.

So next year I'm staying in and watching TV.

Yours

Benny Benson

Dear Mr and Mrs Benson

I am so sorry not to have seen Benny at Sunday School recently. He certainly was a real live-wire to have around. Although his continually loud singing of:

"While Shepherds washed their socks by
night,
The sheep could not be found,
They'd done a bunk and left the town,
From pongs that hung around",

won't be missed.

Also, could you please check Little Elvis's pockets before sending him to the Tiny Tots' Sunday School, because we have found him handing out earthworms as presents to several small girls, and Miss Comstock, the Sunday School Teacher, came over quite faint when one turned up in her cup of tea.

Hoping to hear from you,

Reverend G Plumrose

BENNY BENSON'S
NEW YEAR RESOLUTIONS

1. I promise not to drop my toy bombs around the house,
    especially when Grandma is in the toilet.

2. I will not bounce my ball against the outside wall
    when Mum has one of her headaches in the kitchen.

3. Me and Philip Stocks will not use Dad's bed as a
    trampoline, because it brings out the springs and
    Dad rips his bum to pieces.

4. I will not keep building tents in the back garden out
    of Mum's best maternity dresses.

5. I promise to eat all my Brussells sprouts and not
    drop them in the goldfish bowl when no one is looking,
    because then the goldfish have got no room to move.

6. I will not pretend that the stairs are Mount Everest

and put bits of lino on them, because then Grandma goes sliding out the front door.

7. I will *not* ever again tie Grandma's knitting to the cat's tail, because he goes climbing and leaves woolly socks all over Mr Jones's chimney pots.

8. I will *not* be bored, even if I am, and not ever, ever again use Mum's sponge cake as a dart board and spear it with Grandma's knitting needles.

9. I will not put a clothes peg on my dad's nose for a laugh when he is snoring. Because it are frightening waking up suddenly with something gripping your nose, ain't it? But also because he will bury me up to my neck in the rose beds if I does it again.

Dear Doctor Cummings

Please could you come to see my dad because of his
snoring at night?

It is so loud the whole house shakes.

When my friend Philip came to stay he said, "What's
that noise? It sounds like a train is coming up the stairs."

I said, "It's only my dad snoring."

We've got to do something quick because my mum
said, "Your dad is driving me round the bend with his
snoring."

Last night she was hitting him with her rubber water
bottle and shouting, "Shut up the flamin' row!" And
Dad said, "What did I do?"

He don't even know that he snored.

Perhaps we could try sticking something up his nose,
because that's where the noise comes from.

Or maybe my dad would be best in the garden shed
at night?

My mum said, "No, it's best he's sent to the North
Pole or Mount Everest!"

What's really interesting is that my dad keeps saying that he don't snore. When he says that, Grandma says, "They should have cut off your nose at birth. It makes more noise than an atomic bomb."

Yours

Slug Benson

Dear Philip Stocks

This is a secret letter about our gang what we started.

What I wants you to do is sneak around and see how many spies you can find in Milton Keynes. Probably most of them live up near Bletchley station, because most spies got to escape some time and a station is the best place.

Also, I got a suspicion about our teacher. She's always talking about China and other places like that. Perhaps she's preparing to take us away with her to some foreign place so we can be scientists or something.

We must meet up the field later in our den.

Nobody knows about our den, so we can talk in silence. But please don't bring your sister any more because she just keeps saying we are stupid. What's the use of having a spy what goes on like that every ten seconds?

I've got a real problem though because everybody's been listening to Kerry Presswood at school. That Kerry Presswood's been going around saying she's going to marry me. Every time I sneak out anywhere, everyone who sees me says, "Are you going off to get married to Kerry Presswood?" and then falls about laughing.

So it's hard to be a spy when I come out, ain't it?

Your leader

Samson Superslug

January 8th

Dear Liverpool Manager

I am writing to inform you that I am a young footballer what lives in Milton Keynes.

I think your team is brilliant, but so am I.

I scored a goal up the park today against my best friend Philip Stocks. He even said to me, "Cor, Benny, that was brilliant!"

It was at least as good as anything in the World Cup.

Another time, I nearly scored a goal and Philip tripped me up.

I said, "That's a penalty!" and he said, "No, it's not!" And I said, "You're a cheat," and he said, "You stink, anyway."

So we aren't friends any more, but I'm still a brilliant footballer.

Perhaps you would like to put me on trial?

I would really like to play for Liverpool.

Then I could be famous and not go to school any more.

Yours   Samson Superslug

Dear Benny Benson

Thank you for your letter of January 8th.

Applications to join Liverpool Football
Club are usually through a local club
and trial. Scoring a goal on a field
against your friend is not normally
good enough recommendation to
play for England.

Yours sincerely

O Penn

Mrs Olive Penn
Secretary to the Manager

PS I enclose a signed photograph of
the current squad.

Dear Philip

Can you get the gang together?

I've just seen this video about Dracula and vampires. They've got big teeth and they drinks your blood. Also, there's lots of vampires around so we got to watch out. Mrs Reynolds at number 22 is most likely to be one because she's got the biggest teeth you ever saw.

I thought my Grandma might be one too, but she takes her teeth out at night. But just in case, I put an onion on my bed.

You're supposed to have garlic but my mum hasn't got none, so onions will do.

Last night Mum found my onion.

"What's this?" she said.

I said, "It's to stop vampires."

She just laughed and said, "That's only a story."

I hope my mum doesn't get too friendly with Mrs Reynolds or she might turn into a vampire.

It wouldn't be much use having a mum who spends all her time going around biting people for breakfast, would it?

Yours

A Vampire Hunter

Dear Gang

Yesterday, Mrs Reynolds chased me from her garden
when I was investigating in her shed for clues.

I was looking for clues of her being a vampire. But I
found nothing, not even a coffin. When she caught me
she said, "If I ever see you in my garden spying on me
again, I'm going to call the police."

So she's onto us, ain't she?

She guessed we are counter spies.

So lie low for a few days and then resume
operations.

Yours

Slug

Dear Education Department

I am a concerned student of the school timetable.

First, there are too many sums.

My teacher keeps saying, "Benny, get on with your sums and stop talking," but she don't know that I've got to talk to someone because my brain gets stuffed up with sums.

If I don't talk then maybe my brain will explode.

Also, I'm fed up with doing Drama because I've got to pretend to be a tree. Every time we do Drama the teacher says be a tree. I've got to stand still on one foot with my arms held out. And she makes us stay like that for so long that I falls over. Another time she said be a frog and hop around the room, and I fell over again.

What we need is more football.

I don't fall over when I play football and my brain doesn't hurt. Also, I don't talk much. I only shout things like, "You brainless idiot, why don't you watch where you're passing the ball?"

Assembly is no good, either.

Every morning we've got to listen to Mr Hutchins going on about things like the toilets and who left the tap running and flooded them and pulled miles of toilet rolls across the playground. And because he goes on and on about it and says, "I'm going to wait till someone owns up," I got an itch on my bum.

And I said to Philip Stocks, "I got an itch on my bum," and Mr Hutchins said, "Are you owning up, Benny Benson?" And I said, "No, sir, I got an itch on my bum." And everybody laughed and Mr Hutchins said, "Come and see me after Assembly, Benny Benson!"

And I got done.

I got to stay in at break for two weeks.

31

So Assembly is no good because you get done for an itch on your bum. Seems to me it ain't quite fair.

Yours

Superslug

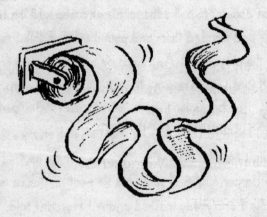

The Education Department
County Hall
Aylesbury

Dear Mr Superslug

In reply to your letter of the 14th we are surprised by your criticisms. Sums have been the central pivot of the timetable since the last century, and we have no plans to abandon them. Drama, of course, is an important means of self-expression. Even the Chief Education Officer has confessed that he was once a lamp-post in a school play.

I take your last point. The education service is attempting to foster a more reverential spirit in the Assembly. The toilets do not normally figure in our thinking.

I hope this answers your queries.

Yours sincerely

F. M. Childs

Mr F M Childs
Education Officer

Dear Mr and Mrs Benson

Could you have a word with your Benny, please? I have been reading stories to the children for weeks now, and have just discovered that he has not been listening to a word. Apparently his mind is too stuffed up with fantasies that he has gleaned from videos. Last week he even told me that William the Conqueror was a secret agent from a James Bond movie.

Yours sincerely

G. Snipe

Ms G Snipe,
B Ed (Hons) Infant Teacher

PS I include a sample of one of his typically muddled stories.

BENNY'S STORY

Once upon a time there was a girl called Red Riding Hood what lived with the Seven Dwarfs in a castle in Transylvania.

And this Wolf were a Dracoola and came and tried to blow their house down and he said, "I'll huff and puff and blow your house down."

But he couldn't do it.

And Red Riding Hood what were a secret agent of the Government said, "What big teeth you got!"

And the wolf said, "All the better to blow your house down with!"

Then a man called James Bond came and killed the wolf with a Q5X laser gun, and they all got married and lived happily ever after.

THE END

by Benny Benson

Dear Philip

I got in real trouble today in school and my teacher got real mad and wrote to my mum.

So I can't come out to our den tonight.

It was because I wrote out the story wrong, the one our teacher's been reading us for weeks now. Apparently she's been reading us "Snow White" and I wrote down "Red Riding Hood and the Seven Dwarfs".

She said, "Don't you listen to *nothing*, Benny Benson?"

And I said, "It were only a mistake."

And she said, "How come you've got a wolf in the story? It's the first time I ever heard of a wolf trying to blow down the house of the Seven Dwarfs. Are you taking the mickey out of me?"

Well, anyone can make a mistake, especially if they're counter-spies, can't they?

Yours
Slug

Dear Mayor of the Council

Today I heard my mum say that she was going to get help
from the Council.

It's about my little brother, Sniffer, who's three.

It's because he's out of control and nobody can do
anything with him. We call him Sniffer because his nose
keeps running and he sniffs and wipes his nose with his
sleeve. Mum says, "Don't do that, Sniffer," but he still
does it. Even when we eat dinner he does it and Aunty
Sue, who came once, said she didn't want no dinner
because she felt sick.

Also, he put worms from the garden up Dad's car
exhaust. And when Dad started up it blew all the
worms over Mum's washing.

And every time we take him to Woolworth's he says
"Give me that toy!" and when Mum says no, he lies on
the floor and screams and kicks his feet. Then everyone
comes up and says, "What've you done to him?" and Mum
says, "Nothing," but they don't believe her. So in the end
she *has* to buy him the toy.

Also, on his birthday, Mum told me to go and put his shoes on him. And I tried but he said no and threw them out of the bedroom window.

And he kept coming up to Mum and saying in front of all my friends that he'd done a poo, just when she went to give out the jelly and custard!

Yours

Samson Superslug

38

Dear Supermarket Manager

I am apologising for my little brother who is a nuisance at the supermarket.

He keeps sliding on the floor and scaring poor old ladies to death. Nobody can stop him.

This lady said to him, "Have you got a mother or not?"

What sort of a question is that?

He's certainly got a mother, but she don't like him. She shouts and screams, but he still slides on the supermarket floor.

Also, he keeps putting things in the trolley when no one is looking. That's how we got twenty packets of tomato soup at the check-out.

Mum said, "How did they get there?"

And the check-out lady said, "If you don't know, I certainly don't."

Finally, I'm sorry that my brother pulled down that

giant pile of toilet rolls that the lady so carefully put up.

It was nearly up to the roof, but my brother still pulled it down, didn't he? I don't think, though, that it were right to say that he should be strung up from the nearest tree.

Shouting like that only made him cry and wet his pants.

Yours

Benny Benson

Dear Prime Minister

We are a fit fighting force what is fighting the enemies
of the Government. There are me what is chief counter-
spy, Philip Stocks what are a giant and body guard,
Sniffer my brother who is three, my cousin Angel and
our dog, Tiger.

   We is all dedicated to the destruction of aliens,
Dracoolas and spies. I hope you will sign us up for the
Government.

   Yours

Benny Benson
Samson Superslug

Dear Mr Superslug

Thank you for your letter. The Prime Minister welcomes any help as long as the laws of this country are not broken.

I hope this answers your query.

Yours sincerely

Emmeline Pankhurst

Emmeline Pankhurst (Ms)
Under Secretary to the Prime Minister

Dear Jim'll Fix It

Please could you fix it for me to have loads of money.
How about fifty million pounds? Then I could buy myself
some new trainers because these ones have got holes in.
Every time I go out, the rain comes in and drowns my
feet.

And could you fix it for my grandad to get some
more hair? His hair keeps falling out ten times a day and
he's nearly bald. He said to me, "Look, Benny, my hair
used to be longer than a horse's tail, now I look like a
snooker ball."

And could you get my dad some new glasses? He's
blind without glasses and last week he ate a worm what
crawled on his dinner plate because he thought it were
a fish-finger. That's how bad his eyes are. And he keeps
waving to people he don't know because he can't see
proper.

And can you fix it for me to meet all the Dracoolas and spies what lives in Milton Keynes. Then my Superslug Gang can destroy them by throwing onions at them.

Yours

Benny Benson

Dear Hospital People

Thanks for looking after my mum when she had a baby.

We all were glad when she came back home because we got fed up with burnt sausages and fish-fingers every day from my dad. He's useless at cooking. He can't even cook a glass of water, he's so bad.

And he didn't iron my football kit properly and everyone laughed when I went to football practice.

Anyway, that baby cried ever since. I didn't know babies cried so much. Even in the middle of the night they cry. And they keep messing their pants and stink the place up.

My friend Philip Stocks said, "Cor, what is that pong?" And I said, "It's only the baby. He done it."

Mum and Dad are shouting at each other at night.

Last night Mum said, "It's your turn to get up tonight to baby," and Dad said, "No, I've got to go to work tomorrow."

Mum said, "What do you think I do all day?" and he

said, "You do nothing," and that made her real mad and she threw the alarm clock at him.

Now everyone comes to our house.

They come to see the baby and they become real stupid. They pull weird faces and say "Coochy coo" and "Blub a lub" and all that. Fancy grown people pulling stupid faces and saying stupid things. When I tried it at school for a laugh, my teacher made me stand in the corridor with my hands on my head.

Yours

Benny the Slug

TOP SECRET

Dear Number Two Counter-spy (lootenant Philip Stocks)

The man who serves me at our shop looks extremely
suspicious to me.

He's got a big moustache and a bald head.

I believe he shaved off his hair and stuck it on his
mouth for a moustache.

He's likely to be a spy.

So watch your change from buying sweets. He must
be getting money from somewhere to pay for his spying.

Yours

Number One Slug

Dear Betty

I've always looked up to you as an
older sister. Could you advise me about
Benny and Little Elvis who are driving
me mad at the moment? Benny is causing
a lot of bother at school. I keep getting
letters from his teachers complaining
about him. And Jim is no help. He's only
worried about winning the Pools and his
next snooker match down the Working
Men's Club. All he says about Benny is
"He's a real boy, isn't he?"

I've tried getting Benny interested
in clubs. He won't go to Cubs any more
because he says he's not having any old
Brown Owls telling him how to tie knots
in stupid bits of string. He's banned from
Blimpton Football Juniors because the
Manager says his idea of good football is

to rugby-tackle everybody to the ground.
And every time I try to talk to him about
his behaviour he says he's got important
work to do as a Dracula hunter.

I tell you, Betty, what with all this and
Elvis bringing in every slimy creature
from the back garden, I'm going crazy!

Perhaps we can get together to talk
about things over a cup of coffee one
afternoon.

Love

Pam

BBC

Dear Benny Benson

It was very nice hearing from you. I enjoyed reading your letter.

However, we are unable to find any spies for you to follow, or any Vampire-hunting for you to do. In fact we are fresh out of vampires and spies at the moment. Also, the last million pounds we had was spent by one of our typists on lunch in the West End and the taxi fare.

Good luck with your Gang. I hope you manage to solve some good mysteries.

Yours sincerely

F. Kenshole

The Producer, "Jim'll Fix It"

PS I am a little puzzled about the onion throwing. Are the spies going to cry themselves to death?

Dear Headmaster

I wish to complain about one of your students.

Kerry Presswood is her name and she kissed me again today. If I asked her once not to do it, I asked her 50 times. But she still does it.

I said, "Don't do that," but she took no notice.

She keeps on saying, "I love you, Benny Benson," and doing it. She creeps up on me when I least expect it and kisses me. You'd think she would be able to control herself being nine now. Once she did it in class and Simon Snoddles saw it and made a noise like an elephant's bum.

Teacher said, "What are you doing, Simon Snoddles?" And he said he didn't say nothing. I know he didn't say nothing but he made a rude noise instead.

Please help me about Kerry Presswood.

Soon she'll be trying to marry me, and I've got no defence against her because she is twice my size and as fat as a dinosaur.

Yours

Benny Benson

PS Also, could you make the tests easier what you are giving us so that I can get everything right? And Philip Stocks needs help because he keeps trying to do his sums upside down, don't he?

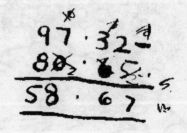

Dear Mr Hutchins

I am writing to explain to you why I was rubbing out the blackboard today.

This was because somebody wrote "Benny Benson Loves Kerry Presswood", which is not true.

If I loved her, would I be trying to get away from her all the time?

The truth is I can't stand her, but nobody believes me.

She's just got it in mind to marry me and I've got it in mind to get to the other end of the earth from her.

Yours

Benny Benson

Child Psychology Unit

Dear Mr Hutchins

Child Psychology Visit

Thank you for your hospitality at the school on Friday. My meeting with young Benny Benson was very interesting.

It was difficult to make a firm decision on Benny's intelligence, mainly because he will not concentrate on anything for any length of time. He also treats everything as a bit of a joke. For example, to my question "What is hot?" he insisted on saying things like "mustard" and "pepper". For "What is cold?" I got the reply "Grandma's heart", and he waited for me to roll around laughing, which of course I did not. A request to do a written test was met with "I can't do tests. They blows my brains out." In the middle of our talk, he suddenly said "Do you want to be in my gang? We're catching spies and vampires and things." Later he added, "If I'm really good and do your test, will you pay me £10?"

He also feels that everybody is against him, especially his teachers, who he calls "Screechers!" because they are always shouting at him. Perhaps a cosy little chat with him might make him feel more at home with schoolwork.

Yours

Harold Horowitz

Harold Horowitz
Child Psychologist

Dear Psychiatrist

Please would you come and see my big brother, who is fifteen.

I think he is mentally ill.

First, I'm real fed up of him staring into space and groaning.

Dad says it's because he's in love with Diane Trock from down the road. She's real ugly, but when I said that to my brother he went crazy and tried to kill me.

Do you think that's sane, to try and kill your younger brother with a football pump?

Also, he don't eat his food.

He just plays with it and groans.

I tried doing that when I got cabbage and my mum nearly went barmy.

Seems there's one rule for him and another for me.

Yours faithfully

Benny Benson

PS I've got a problem too. A great monster with little legs, a massive body and dressed in green and pink stripes is trying to get me. Her name is Kerry Presswood and she says she loves me. But when she kisses me she sucks so hard she drains all the blood out of me, don't she?. I become all dried out and can't move for hours. So please help, or soon I will be a little dried prune lying on the floor.

Blimpton Primary School

Dear Mrs Benson

I must ask you to have a serious chat with your son, Benny. As I have told you on many occasions, he is buried in a world of his own. Only last week he was made to stand in the corridor with his hands on his head for saying that his teacher was a "secret agent from Dracula". In Assembly yesterday he stood up and informed the whole school that he was spying for the Government, and that the teachers were aliens from outer space.

I know that all this is the result of a powerful imagination, but we also suspect him of secretly flooding the toilets so that he can have days off school to search for "Giant Octopuses from Mars", as he calls them. Also, he has disrupted Drama lessons and School Plays by deliberately falling over while pretending to be a tree. Once at school dinners, he insisted loudly that the tomato sauce he was using was vampire's blood, and put all the children off their food.

I must confess, we are almost at our wits' end.

I hope you can help with our little problem.

Yours

B C Hutchins

B C Hutchins
Headmaster

Our school caretaker, Grizzly Grimswood, who never shaves and has got a bald head, is always moaning. He says the floor is never clean enough because of our muddy shoes, and keeps polishing and polishing so much that now it's like an ice-rink. And yesterday the Chairman of the Governors came, who's a real old lady what can hardly walk, and she went sliding the whole way down the corridor and into the Gents' toilet without knocking, and sat on Mr Hutchins' lap, who was in there. I never heard such screaming in all my life. So now we've got to take our shoes off when we go in school because Grizzly can't polish the floor no more.

February 28th

To Mrs Benson

Can you keep your Benny under control, please? He keeps creeping into my back garden at night with his friends and dropping onions on the lawn. I'm sick of it. In the supermarket once he dropped six onions in my trolley when my back was turned. Why he does it, I don't know.

I have enough troubles of my own without all this happening. If it doesn't stop soon, I shall have to inform the authorities.

Yours

Mrs Reynolds

Mrs Reynolds

Dear Grandma

I'm so sorry that the puss done a poo on your knitting. He keeps finding your knitting to do a poo on, don't he? Perhaps from when he was a baby puss, he thought that it was the only place in the whole world to do it.

Actually he's improving lately.

On Monday, Mum said, "What's that smell in here. Is it your socks?"

And Dad said, "No, it's not, these are clean on today."

We looked behind the sideboard and found puss had done a poo. That's the first time he didn't do it on your knitting, so that's good, ain't it? Anyway, I hope you don't chase him with your knitting needle again. He's like a streak of lightning, ain't he? How he got up on the sideboard so quick, goodness knows.

Your grandson

Benny

The Police Station <u>Bletchley</u>

Dear Mr and Mrs Benson

This is to inform you that we have had reports of your son, Benny, creeping through people's back gardens in the early winter evenings. We have talked to him and he has told us that he is "only helping the police because he is a Government Agent". He also says that he is worried that you, his parents, may end up as "Slaves of Dracula", or "Space Monsters with bulging eyes and tentacles".

He informs me that part of the trouble seems to be his grandma, who, he says, is always knitting socks too big for anyone to wear, and who keeps waking up in the middle of the night and shouting "Who turned out the lights?" in a very loud voice.

All this is making him feel very insecure.

I hope I can leave the matter in your very capable hands.

Yours sincerely

P C Wibble
Local Policeman

Dear Philip

It looks like we got to stop some of our important
activities.

Like creeping through back gardens to get
information.

My mum said, "I hope you're not one of those boys
who's being a nuisance in gardens. Because you'll get no
pocket money if I find that out." And I can't lose my
pocket money, can I? Nobody can survive without pocket
money. Everybody knows that. And Mrs Reynolds is on
to us ain't she? She knows we are counter-spies and
know she is a Dracula.

Anyway, we've got enough problems in our house.

Mum is always arguing with Grandma. She says she
keeps pinching Baby's Gripe Water because it contains
gin or something. That's what makes you drunk, ain't it?

It's probably why our baby's been so happy recently and gurgling so much.

Yours

Ben the Slug

PS Get the gang down the field and we can do some football practice. Being fit is good for agents of the Government, ain't it?

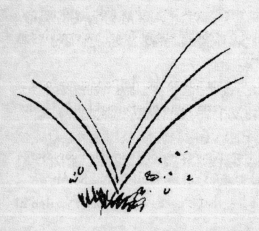

Dear PC Jones

I'm writing in my defence about my next-door
neighbour, Mr Thomas.

It weren't my fault that he was in his garden when
my ball hit him on the head. And why should I take the
blame when he headed the ball into his own rose-beds?
From the fuss he made you'd think prize roses was more
important than human beings.

Instead of going on about calling the police and all
that, just because of roses, he should have apologised for
getting my ball punctured.

And can I remind you, sir, that he didn't give me my
ball back? That is probably enough to get him executed in
some countries.

Also, he called me names like, "Little squirmy toad"
and "Nauseating worm", and others what I didn't hear
properly.

Also, Mr Thomas made my dog bark. He's very fierce
when aroused. But it's not my fault that he bit Mr
Thomas on the leg. That is because Mr Thomas shouted at

my dog and said he is a mangy cur. Next minute my dog bit him, just before Mr Thomas tried to hit him with the garden spade. But he didn't get him because my dog ran like the wind and escaped.

It were like a miracle.

And I saw it all with my own eyes.

So perhaps you will use this for my defence and put it all on my account.

Yours truthfully

Benny Benson, known as The Slug

Dear Minister of Education

I am an agent of the Government what fights Draculas and don't take no nonsense.

I wish to register my objection to teachers reading stories about animals talking and all that.

Everyone knows animals don't say nothing.

Show me one animal that says, "Good morning" and "Hello" and raises its hat when you pass by.

I bet you can't.

My teacher keeps reading *The Wind in the Willows* to us, by Kenny Grahame, and all the animals say, "Hello mate" and "Pass the butter" and all that.

Instead, tell her to read adventure stories and stories about football and gangs and things.

Yours respectfully

Benny the Slug

County Education Dept

Dear Mr Slug

Thank you for your letter. We in the Department feel that you have a point. Fostering the idea that some animals talk could lead to children viewing their pets as second-class animals. Such discrimination is unacceptable, and there seems to be a case for banning such books.

Please keep this letter under your hat. There has been some rather unfair criticism of our thinking in the press of late.

I am

Sincerely yours

Deborah P Wingate

Deborah P Wingate

Dear Prime Minister

I've got the answer to all your problems, haven't I?

The Government needs money and I thought of a good idea with our gang down the den last night. Philip Stocks said, "Cor, Benny Benson, you're brilliant, ain't you?" But he always says that, being as he can't think of much else to say.

What we got to do is collect all the left-overs from school dinners what nobody wants, and give them to all the poor people who've got no jobs. They've got lots of left-overs at school. Most people leave their brussels and cabbage, and Faisal Malik always flicks his carrots across the table for a laugh. Also, every plate's got tomato sauce left on it.

So what we've got to do is collect all that together and send it to London to give to the poor people instead of giving them Social Security. Then you've got that money to run the country, haven't you?

71

My fee for this advice can be used for our gang what is protecting your country.

Yours respectfully

Benny Benson

10 Downing Street
London

Dear Mr Benson

We are very happy to hear of the Society you have formed to help with our country's financial problems. Is this some sort of Think-Tank within the Education Service?

As to your suggestion, there *are* problems, here. It would not be acceptable to mix all the left-overs for distribution. There would be a national outcry. For example, tomato sauce would not go well with rhubarb and custard, would it? Unless, of course, we could market the mixture as a completely new food product.

However, we thank you for your suggestions, and welcome new ones.

Yours sincerely

D A Dreme
Prime Minister's Office

Dear Swimming Teacher

I'm just writing to explain to you why I can't swim.

First, I'm scared of being in the water.

You keep saying I must let go of the side and when I let go of the side, I sink. I know you are not trying to drown me, but someone might think so, looking on.

And you also said, "Human beings don't sink because of the air in them." Well, probably I'm different because I've got no air left in me.

It's also embarrassing because all the class was watching when I tried to swim a width. I swum two strokes and then I sank, and when I came up for air you said, "Well done, Benny, keep going."

And all I wanted to say was, "Help, I'm drowning!"

But I sank again and when I came up again I was on the other side. Everybody clapped and said, "Well done, Benny," when actually I nearly drowned.

Anybody would think I won the Olympics.

So I hope you will never expect me to go in the water again. Next time might be my last.

Yours

Benny Benson

PS Is it right that you is trying to drown an important servant of the Government?

BENNY BENSON

SPRING TERM SCHOOL REPORT

ENGLISH
Reading: Benny's reading is coming on well, but he appears only to be interested in horror stories and books about boys' gangs.
Writing: Very untidy. Will not concentrate on handwriting. Powerful imagination.
Spelling: This needs considerable attention.

DRAMA
Keeps playing the fool. Falls over when I ask him to be just about anything. A natural clown (unfortunately).

MATHS
Benny has an aversion to number work. He keeps sneaking a calculator in to do all his sums on. Also natters incessantly.

SPORTS
Benny is enthusiastic about all sport. He is very sexist, though, saying that netball is a

"dumb girl's game". He shouts a lot in football matches and is aggressive.

GENERAL BEHAVIOUR
Very disruptive. Takes every opportunity to set the class off into giggles.

Ms G Snipe, Class Teacher

HEADMASTER'S COMMENT
Benny's behaviour is appalling. He seems to spend most of his life in the corridor with his hands on his head.

B C Hutchins

Dear Teddy Bear

I hope you don't mind me writing to you.

It seems stupid writing to a Teddy Bear what can't talk nor listen to nobody. But I've got no one else at the moment because Philip Stocks has gone to stay with his auntie for a while.

It's because I'm sick of school and being drowned in Swimming.

My teacher said again that I must go and stand in the corridor with my hands on my head. She only did that because she don't like me.

She actually said, "I don't like you, Benny Benson." She said it because I splashed Kerry Presswood when I played sand and water. And because she cried.

She did it last time I splashed her too.

And the time before that when I splashed paint on her white blouse. She is just a misery, that Kerry Presswood.

She even told me off when I threw her ball on the school roof. Then when I went to climb to get it she

78

went and told Miss Spruggins, what's got a boil on her nose.

And Miss Spruggins told me to stand by the wall with my hands on my head.

Seems to me that all they want you to do in school is stand with your hands on your head.

Probably if the Queen came to that school they'd make her go and stand in the corner, with her hands on her head.

When I grow up I'm going to be in the Government and come to this school and make all the teachers stand with their hands on their heads.

Yours

Superslug

Dear Philip

Please don't take any notice of what they're saying in
the papers - it's not true. I did not save Kerry
Presswood from drowning. I was just sitting on the
riverbank, fishing and minding my own business, when she
jumped out on me and shouted, "Boo! Benny Benson, I
love you!"

That's when I fell in the river from the shock and
because she pushed me. Then she fell after me and
nearly flattened me by her weight.

It were like a Great Whale fell on me, or even the
QE2! And I nearly drowned. But she got out and went
home and I got out too. Mainly because the water only
comes up to your knees. And this man said, "Cor, little
boy, what's your name☐ You just saved that little girl. It
were the bravest thing I've ever seen." I tried hard to
tell him that she just sat on me, but he took no notice.

He told the newspaper and they sent someone
round to talk to me. And I said that I didn't do nothing.

But they didn't believe me. They said that I am a hero.
And it's all because a whale sat on me.

Your pal

Superslug

Boy Saves Girl from Drowning!

Yesterday it was reported to us by a Mr David Glibbons, 42, of Blimpton Angling Society that Benny Benson, aged 9, of 3, Park Walk, Blimpton, dived into the River Mee on Sunday and saved Kerry Presswood, aged 9, from drowning.

With no regard for his own safety he leapt from the bank where he had been fishing and raised the small girl's head above the water. Mr Glibbons said, *"It was an heroic act, the bravest thing I ever saw in my life. The little boy did not hesitate for an instant. He deserves a medal."*

There was no comment from Benny's Headmaster yesterday, but his mother said, *"He's always throwing himself into things."*

THE MOON NEWSPAPER

BOY OF 9 DEFIES DEATH TO RESCUE HELPLESS CHILD!

Two days ago, Benny Benson, aged 9, a boy whose headmaster says "suffers from some grave problems", threw himself into the swirling waters of the River Mee to save little Kerry Presswood, aged 9, from drowning. Near to drowning himself, frail Benny held up the head of the tiny tot until she could climb back up the riverbank to safety. An observer of the incident, Dave Glibbons, 42, said, *"This must rank as one of the Bravest Acts in the History of Mankind. If this boy were old enough he would receive the Victoria Cross."*

Benny Benson is a modest little chap who insisted that he did nothing.

No doubt, however, he will be in line for one of the Prizes in this year's Bravest Child in Britain Awards, presented by the Princess at Buckingham Palace in two months' time.

Buckingham Palace
London

Dear Benny Benson,

The Bravest Child in Britain Awards

This is to inform you that you have been nominated by The Moon newspaper, and accepted, as one of the Bravest Children in Britain for this year. Consequently, I invite you to attend the Award Ceremony on May 12th at which Her Royal Highness the Princess will present a medal and certificate. There will also be a prize for the whole family, to be announced later.

Yours sincerely

Philip Slipper
Philip Slipper
PPS to the Princess

Dear Susan Philpot

Please would you like to come to my birthday party?

    All the rest coming are boys, but Mum says I've got to ask you because you are our next-door neighbour, and your mum and mine are friends. And if I don't ask you your mum might be jealous and not speak to her.

    She said, "Anyway, I once played with you."

    But that was years ago when I was three years old and a bit stupid.

    I said, "I don't like her," but she said that that doesn't matter and even if I do think you're a stupid girl, I've still got to invite you.

    I hope you bring me a good present.

    I don't want no doll or something real stupid like that.

Your next-door neighbour

Benny Benson

PS My mum just said that my cousin's got to come, the one what lives up Stoney Stratford and keeps saying, "Ith abtholutely dithguthting" about everything. So you won't be the only girl. She's the girl what was in our Gang once. But we had to get rid of her because every time we made a plan, like hunting for Dracula and putting a spike through his heart, or shooting space monsters with our ray-gun, she kept saying, "We can't do that." And we said, "Why not?" And she said, "Becoth ith abtholutely dithguthting." So we said, "You're an enemy alien and have got to be destroyed," and she ran off home, didn't she?.

Dear Grandma

I would like to apologise for all the bad things I've done to you this year.

Perhaps then you might be able to give me a birthday present tomorrow.

First, I done a bad thing the other day when I walked in the house in my muddy football boots and stepped on your pink knitting. It were not deliberate, I assure you.

Another time I was collecting ladybirds for my ladybird zoo that me and Philip Stocks done.

It were most unfortunate that I left the whole collection on your bed by mistake and they all escaped. Then when you went to bed they crawled all over you in the middle of the night.

I believe that some of then even bit you, but I cannot be blamed for that, can I?

That was a bad night for me because all the screaming woke me up. And was it right to say to a poor child that he should be flushed down the loo?

Sometimes I think you don't like me because you keep complaining at me and saying how you didn't do those things when you were my age. Perhaps you didn't complain about things like eating cabbage, and you didn't make noises all the way up the stairs, pretending to be an aeroplane. Anyway Dad says you are a moaning minny, but I think it's probably natural, being as you are very old and worn out.

So I hope you will see your way to giving me a good present.

Your grandson

Benny

PS Perhaps you could donate about £2000 from your week's pension to our club funds, because we've got to build a hut instead of meeting in those stupid bushes up in the park. We need protection from Kerry Presswood and her lot, who keep interrupting important meetings about how our gang can help the Prime Minister save the economy.

Dear Teddy Bear

Weren't it nice on my birthday trip to the seaside?
Except that the train journey was long and boring.

Mum said, "Why don't they have more toilets on long,
boring train journeys?" That's because she couldn't get to
wee because of the queue, wasn't it? She sat for the
whole journey looking like she'd just stepped on a six-
inch nail?

At the Fair I bunged you off the Big Wheel, didn't I?
And you didn't say nothing, even when you went SPLAT
on the ground. Dad says you are brave, but I think you
are a bit brainless.

Only brainless bears don't speak when someone
splats them from two hundred feet up.

Also, everybody went on donkeys, except Grandma.
That's because she's too fat and would probably drive
the poor thing down in the sand instead of up the beach.

Least, that's what Dad says.

Your own friend

Superslug

Dear Vicar

Can you come and talk to my dad about his trouble with getting lost on car trips?

Every time we go to a big town like Southend, my dad gets lost and we keep going round and round.

Once we passed Woolworths ten times and I said, "We passed here again, Dad." And he said, "I know, I know, shut up!"

Even my mum said, "We are dying a death in this car without a drink."

And my dad said a rude word to her.

So my mum said, "Stop the car, and get out, all of you."

And my dad said, "Don't be silly."

And we caught a train home, leaving my dad with the car.

I said, "Will we see my dad again?"

And my mum said, "I hope not."

But when we got home, Dad was there.

And Dad said, "I am sorry," and they kissed.

Parents are real weird, ain't they? Certainly, when I got my James Bond car I'm not going to get lost on special missions, am I?

Yours

Benny Benson

Dear Police

Can you protect me from Michael Smith, who lives down our road?

I am an innocent boy doing innocent things when up comes Michael Smith, and squirts me with this water-pistol and says, "Get lost, pigface," and runs off. What ain't very respectful to Britain's Bravest Boy, what is also an agent of the Government.

He did that one million times last week.

When I told my dad he just laughed and said, "Perhaps he thinks you need a wash."

I don't think saying that is helpful when I've got problems.

Actually, I'm fed up of my dad and his sense of humour. If I had a son who was suffering bad mental health from Michael Smith, I wouldn't say stupid things like that.

Perhaps you could come down our road and put the fright of God in Michael Smith?

Then I can sleep sound at night.

Yours

Benny Benson

The Police Station Bletchley

Dear Benny Benson

In answer to your complaint, we have placed the County Police Force on full alert, a squad of police cars has surrounded the area, and the SAS is on stand-by. We will leave no stone unturned to make sure that this vicious criminal is apprehended, and his weapon taken from him. Then we can all sleep safe in our beds.

Yours sincerely

P.C. Fred Jones

PC Fred Jones
for The Home Secretary

BBC

Dear Mr and Mrs Benson

Following the announcement of your son's *Bravest Child in Britain* award, we invite you to appear with Benny and the rest of your family on the "TV Morning" programme at 8.10 am on May 15th.

To assist you in being punctual on the programme we will pay all expenses to place you and your family overnight in the Hotel Splendide in The Strand, London. On the morning in question a company car will convey the family to the Television Studio.

Please could you confirm your acceptance of this date.

Yours sincerely

S Ferguson

S Ferguson
Researcher

Dear Aunty Betty

It was nice to see you yesterday, but my cousin Angela is really annoying with her doll what says, "Mama!" and wets itself.

How can a sensible person sit and watch TV when someone keeps pulling that string on the doll that says, "Mama!"

I can't get to sleep because I think I keep hearing "Mama! Mama!" all the time.

Also, Angela keeps on talking to that doll and saying "Who's Mummy's little baby then?" and pushing the poor doll up and down the garden path in its doll's pram saying, "Let's go to the shops now." She's got a powerful imagination, that Angela.

But if she keeps talking to herself any more they might say she's barmy.

So perhaps you could give her some talking to.

Your nephew

Benny

PS Also, your daughter is really ungrateful, ain't she? When I tried to give her one of my pear drops that I've been saving in my pocket from last Tuesday, she said, "Ith abtholutely dithguthting." She keeps on saying that, don't she? I've seen her playing doctors and nurses with her Winnie-the-Pooh teddy bear and she was doing a heart operation. Seems to me doctors don't say, "Itha btholutely dithguthting," when they're taking out people's hearts, do they? Perhaps she needs an operation on her brain instead. What is worse is, she is one of our agents in the Superslug gang. Since when did James Bond take a doll what says "Mama, mama" on secret missions?

April 16th

Dear Vicar

It's about our play that we are doing at the Sunday
School, called "Joseph and his Technicolour Dream
Coat". It's really good with singing and all that stuff, but
it would be much better with some monsters in, or spies,
or perhaps someone could dress up as Gazza and
pretend to be a footballer in Pharaoh's Court?

Also, I wish to complain about Willy Snebbings what
plays Joseph, and I've got to throw him in the pit.

He says, "Don't you hit me on the head like that
again, Benny Benson, or you're a dead duck."

First, I don't know what he means by a dead duck,
do I? Also, he knows I can smash him up any time he
wants. So why does he say it? It's because he knows I'm
not allowed to bash him in the middle of a play, isn't it?

He's a right prat, is Willy Snebbings.

Yours

Benny Benson

PS I don't think it is fair all these problems because I got enough already, what with Kerry Presswood trying to marry me. And I got enough work trying to protect this country from enemies of the Government.

April 19th

Buckingham Palace
London

Dear Mr and Mrs Benson

The Bravest Child in Britain Awards

I am pleased to inform you that we have awarded Benny, yourselves and the rest of your family, a holiday for two weeks in Wales. Further details will be forwarded in due course.

We have taken the further step of including the Presswood family in the package holiday, so that the little girl can be with her saviour for two weeks. We look forward to seeing you and your little boy at the ceremony next month.

I am,
Yours sincerely

Philip J Slipper

Philip J Slipper

Dear Zookeeper

I've been to your zoo today. It were Grandma's present
for becoming Britain's bravest boy.

Actually I got dragged there by my Grandma what
loves zoos. She doesn't love nothing else, just loves zoos.

Surprisingly, the animals all disappeared when they
saw her coming. Even the tigers went and hid in the
grass.

Grandma said, "Look, there's a tiger in the grass,"
and I said, "What? Where?" because I couldn't see
nothing.

Seems to me tigers don't like people looking at them,
especially Grandma, so they go and hide.

Anyway, giraffes don't hide.

We saw them.

Even if they tried, they couldn't hide being as they've
got great long necks. One giraffe reached down, and
Grandma made such a big fuss she probably thought it
wanted to bite her head off. But it didn't, it only
wanted to eat her hair.

Anyway, I like sharks.

I've seen "Jaws" on TV but your shark wasn't very big. On TV, Jaws could just about eat an elephant. Your shark would have had difficulty eating a fish-finger.

I said to Grandma, "Where's the shark?" and she said, "There." And I saw this titchy fish that kept being chased by a big goldfish.

I wish to complain about you cheating people by saying you've got a shark. You should say that you've got a really titchy little shark that's frightened by goldfish.

I like monkeys best, especially the ones with purple bums. Grandma said, "You've got to say 'posterior' instead of bum." So I wrote in my diary at school "posterior" and when I read it out to the whole class nobody knew what I was talking about.

My teacher couldn't explain because she was laughing so much she nearly fell on the floor.

And all the teachers came and said, "What's

going on?" and she told them. Then they started laughing and going red in the face.

Seems to me teachers have got a weird sense of humour.

Yours faithfully

Samson Superslug

PS Can you find Grandma's false teeth what she sneezed into the polar bear pit? We all had to hold her back from climbing down there to get them. Though my dad didn't try to stop her. He just said he felt sorry for the poor bears if she got near them.

Department of Environmental Health

Dear Mr Benson

Having had several complaints about the barking of your dalmatian dog, my Inspector, Mr Fawlds, came to investigate yesterday. The door was opened by a small boy of about nine years who said, "My dog's got no brains," when asked about the barking. Suddenly, a large spotted dog bounded out of the house and leapt on the Inspector, knocked him down and licked off his glasses, swallowing them.

No harm will come to your dog. The glasses were plastic and will pass out in time, but they did cost £75, and Mr Fawlds seeks compensation. Could you please forward this amount to our office, or we will have to take appropriate action.

Mr Fawlds is also depressed because he had to drive his car back to the office without glasses and consequently drove through a Mr Thomas's front garden, destroying his prize roses.

I am hoping to hear from you,

A S Rayn
Chief Inspector

The production of the play "Joseph and his Technicolour Dream Coat" in the Village Hall by the Methodist Sunday School was an excellent affair. Produced by the Reverend Peabody with musical accompaniment by Mrs Elisand Pryke, the singing was good and most of the acting well-rehearsed. Progress was temporarily halted at one point, when a fight broke out between Joseph and another boy just after Joseph was thrown in the pit. They were eventually separated by Pharaoh who ran on stage wearing head-dress, trainers and a T-shirt bearing the slogan "Yah, Boo, I see You" on the back.

A collection was taken in aid of the Missionary Relief Fund.

Village Fête Announcement

A charity Cricket Match between "The Old Codgers" and "Blimpton School Boys" will be held on May 2nd, in the afternoon. The proceeds will go to the Church Maintenance Fund.

Dear Vet

I've seen programmes about vets on TV and you come to help people who've got problems with animals.

We've got trouble with our dog who's an absolute nutcase. Also, he hasn't got any brains, which ain't much good for an agent of the Samson Superslug gang.

We are especially fed up with him barking at nothing. We are sitting quietly watching TV when all of a sudden he barks like mad and runs to the back door. When we open the door there's nothing there.

We say, "Go get him, killer!" but he runs and hides behind the sofa.

Dad says his brain has gone because he keeps chasing his tail. Probably thinks it is a sausage or something.

And usually he is an abject coward and runs away from everything, even the postman and next door's cat.

But once he decided that Dad was a burglar and wouldn't let him out of the bathroom for two hours.

Dad said, "Let me out, you brainless mutt!"

But that dog went on barking at him.

Dad couldn't get to work that day. He said, "I'm going to skin that dog alive."

Could you please come round and inject him with something so he gets his brains back?

Yours

Samson Superslug

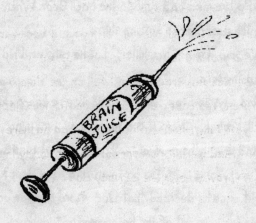

Dear Vicar

It wasn't my fault that the Cricket Match went wrong.

First, when I went back to get ready to bowl to you, I was out of sight down the hill and accidentally fell in a hole by a blackberry bush. So when I finally got out and ran up to bowl, you weren't looking and the ball hit you on the head. That's when you fell on the ground, saying you saw angels in the sky. I didn't see anyone though, only sparrows flying around.

Next time the ball flew out of my hand backwards and hit a poor old lady what was eating her strawberries and cream. Then I fell on the stumps and broke them. We got no others so the match was finished.

It wasn't my fault, was it, that you had no more stumps? And were it right for our captain to say that Britain's bravest boy were a clumsy clod?

Yours

Benny

LETTER TO THE QUEEN

Dear Queen

I am a humble agent of the Government with a gang what is protecting your great land. Thank you for letting me see your daughter, the Princess, next week. Please could you not ask Kerry Presswood because she keeps chasing me. I know I'm supposed to have saved her from drowning but it's a lie. She pushed me in the water then fell in herself and sat on me.

Also, please excuse my dad, who says he doesn't like you. He's not worth much, as my mum says every Friday night when he comes home drunk, dancing down the road and singing, "I'm a blue toothbrush, you're a pink toothbrush." And my mum won't let him in the house. She says, "Push off, you hairy gorilla." And he starts singing, "How much is that doggy in the window?" Then he falls in the fishpond and sits there laughing like an eejit.

I came to Buck House once, and you waved at me in

the crowd. Perhaps one day you will let me in there to be knighted, when I am famous like Gazza. Then I can ride on a white horse to America and fight dragons. They've got them there because I saw them on TV with David Attenborough, who nearly got done to death by a gorilla once.

Your humble servant

Benny Benson

PS Where do you do your shopping? Is it at Tesco, because we might see you there one day. If I meet you I will give you my best conker - it's a one-hundreder, though it's gone a bit green now. Also, could you be President of our gang, then perhaps Samantha Priddy (who's very pretty) would take notice of me and not say I'm a loud-mouthed lout.

Yesterday a catastrophe struck Blimpton Village when a water main burst and flooded Main Street. Several shops were awash and will take days to recover from the effects of the water. The local fair was washed out and has had to be held over for a few weeks.

Dear Water Board

Why can't you look after your water pipes properly?
They flooded our street. We had good fun, though. I
made a boat from a dustbin lid and floated in
through the chip-shop door. Mrs Jones said to me,
"Get out of here, you little tyke," and tried to hit me
with a piece of cod. But she only made me fall in the
water and get my clothes wet, and my mum nearly
killed me. Are that a way to treat a famous kid what
saves the world?

Later my gran tried to wade through to Bingo and nearly got washed down the river and out to sea. That's what your pipe's done, ain't it?

Yours

Benny Benson,
Super Agent

Dear Gang

This is a News letter about being at the Hotel
Splendide in London. The TV are paying for it and we
all came along. It's real posh here. They've got
bedrooms with toilets and bathrooms in them, so you
can have a bath and go to the toilet and go to sleep all
at the same time.

My little brother brought some worms from our
garden in his pocket and gave them to the manager.
We didn't know he'd done that until the manager
nearly went sick on the floor.

Today we went on TV.

Anna Pearl was on too. She asked us about me
being brave. And she said to my brother, "Are you
brave too?" and he didn't answer. He only kept
picking his nose. We tried to stop him but he kept on
doing it.

Anyway, the food was nice.

In the hotel we can take as much as we like and my

little brother put forty pickled onions on his plate with his bacon and egg.

    Yours

Benny the Slug

TV Critic's Choice

Yesterday's only highspot amongst a bleak TV programme was the appearance on "TV Morning" of the Benson family, who enlivened a generally dull programme by their sheer down-to-earth appearance and conversation. It was a delight to watch the expression on Anna Pearl's face as each question she carefully directed at the family was punctuated by the loud voice of the three-year-old saying to her, "My dad don't like you!" every few minutes. Benny Benson, the hero of this saga, finally brought the lid down on Miss Pearl's unruffled calm by declaring to every question she put to him that the girl he saved was, *A dangerous dinosaur what sat on my head. She should be sent to a desert island where she can't hurt no one.* With such simple words are great interviewers laid to rest.

Dear Aunty Val

This is a letter to thank you for the present you sent me.

Mum says I've got to write to you because it's rude not to say thank you. I liked the book that you sent me, only I can't read it. Mum said that *Watership Down* are a classic book, but they should make it easier to read so children can find out what on earth it's all about.

By the way, I did quite well at Sports Day. I came second to Della Mann in the Egg and Spoon race. I would have won but my egg fell off the spoon just before the tape and Della Mann trod on it. She said she didn't mean to do it but knowing Della Mann, she done it accidental on purpose.

I also came second in the Running. At least the teacher said I came second. I thought I won easily, but this teacher said I came second. She don't like me so she said I came second instead of first.

In the Dad's Race my dad came last. He actually fell over twice.

Why my dad goes in for running races, I don't know - except to show me up.

Your nephew

Benny

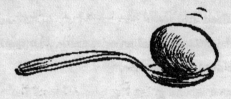

Dear Ted

I am writing to you to explain things. It aren't much good
writing to Philip Stocks all the time because I got to
explain everything about twenty times when I next sees
him.

Now I am Britain's Bravest Boy I got some respect
in this country and I can tell everyone about all the
Draculas, aliens and spies in this beautiful town of
Milton Keynes. But it are surprising how little people
knows about all this. Sometimes they laughs at me so much
I thinks that I is some comedian or something. Perhaps I
got a new career doing jokes on TV.

Benny, the Slug, Benson

Dear Mrs Benson

This is just a note to say how pleased I have been with Benny's behaviour recently. He has become quite a pillar of society since he achieved national fame as Britain's Bravest Boy.

However, I do feel that all this attention has gone a little to his head. He keeps raising his hands in Assembly and asking to speak to the whole school. When he does it's usually to tell us all how he believes that he has saved the whole world from destruction by frightening off various assortments of people and animals who are either aliens or spies. "How do we know," he said once, "that the Queen Mother is not a Monster from outer space in disguise?"

However, I feel that this phase will soon pass. In the meantime, good luck on your holiday in two weeks time. It is well deserved!

Yours sincerely

B C Hutchins

B C Hutchins
Headmaster

Dear Summer Fete Organiser

Did my raffle ticket win that car or not?

I paid 10p for it, so I hope to see some return. I don't
want the car because I can't drive, but I could sell it
and buy my mum a new dress.

She said to my dad, "I haven't had a new dress for
ten years. All I get is from jumble sales."

Also, I wish to apologise for my dad, who is always
showing off.

He said, "I'm going to win the Welly Wanging. It's a
cinch." But he fell over as he threw the boot and it went
and hit the Vicar who was judging the Beautiful Baby
contest. And my baby brother didn't win as Beautiful
Baby. Mainly because he is so ugly, ain't it?

Finally, if you find a strawberry lolly in the grass, it's
mine. Perhaps you could return it because I only licked it
twice.

Yours

Benny Slug Benson

PS I suppose you heard of me, ain't you? I am Britain's Bravest Boy what heads a famous fighting force for saving the world. I got the Prime Minister's personal approval for my daring activities. Though, seeing as I is doing so much, he don't finance me much, do he? A few million pounds would be useful, wouldn't it?

School Diary

On Saturday, we went to the Fair.

I went on the Mexican Hat ride with my dad.

I said, "I don't want to go on," but he said, "Come on, you big baby."

So I went and when we got off my dad was sick. He was sick all over this lady's little dog.

He said, "Sorry, lady," but she still hit him with her umbrella.

In fact, my dad kept being sick all day.

People kept saying, "Watch out for that drunk."

My big brother went on lots of rides with Diane Trock. He can't leave off cuddling and kissing her - it's real disgusting. Somebody should tell him that there's more important things in life.

My little brother went on the roundabout. He went on a little bus and rang the bell, and when the roundabout stopped he wouldn't come off.

The man said, "Come off, little boy. I got a livin' to earn." But my brother said, "No!" And when the man tried to lift him off he put his ice-cream in his hair.

Later, my cousin, Angela won a teddy bear on the darts. She closed her eyes and just threw. It's lucky she hit the target because she might have killed someone.

Later my little brother was real bad. He stuck Grandma's knitting needle in the bouncy castle and it went down. It was lucky we escaped form that Fair because everyone wanted to kill my brother.

Dear Philip

What I been dreading for weeks is about to happen. Your general, Benny Benson, Samson Superslug, agent of the government, famous worker against the horrors of the dark world, got to go on a stupid holiday with the worst danger what he ever got to face. And that greatest horror are Kerry Presswood. Perhaps she will get lost somewhere, being as we are going to the wilds of Wales. Or maybe the Prime Minister will pass over the latest Government weapon so I can disintegrate her on the foothills of Mount Snowden.

If that don't happen perhaps I can escape on a fishing boat to America.

Your leader

Samson Superslug

Dear Philip

How are you?

Here we are on the sand me and my family and flipping Kerry Presswood and her family. There's miles of it here in Wales. In fact, there's so much, it's real boring.

Sand is probably the most boring thing that was ever invented. There's nothing here but crabs walking sideways. And I've got problems because Kerry Presswood keeps stepping on them an squealing, "Help, Benny. I stepped on a crab!"

I wish she'd step on a flippin' shark and then we might get some peace around here.

And all day long she keeps coming up to me, every five minutes, and saying, "Do you want an ice-cream, Benny?" And, "Isn't it a lovely holiday, Benny?"

Quite honestly I'm sick of ice-cream and being on the beach. Then she runs down to the sea and jumps in, and she's so big she just about splashes it all on the sand. They should make a law that says No Girls as Big as Dinosaurs Should Ever Jump in the Sea, shouldn't they?

Anyway, I just lie and dream that maybe one day I can be a famous footballer and get a big transfer to Italy or Brazil. Then I can live in peace and be happy ever after.

Love

Benny,
The Slug

BENNY'S GLOSSARY OF TERMS

COW
What lives in the field where our gang meets. Animal that lives in a field chewing grass and looking real stupid, and that does a bunk when you try to give it Smarties.

DALMATIAN
Real dumb dog with great blobs all over that keeps wagging its tail, even when you're telling it off, and knocks Dad's dinner off the table.

VICAR
A man who keeps coming from the church and calling me, "little chap", and gets Sniffer's Mars Bar down his shirt and gets peed on by the dog.

GRANDMA

Old lady who sits around moaning all day long, especially about my dad. Walks around at six o'clock every morning without her glasses on saying, "Where's me teeth? Where's me teeth?"

MUM

Lady what burns the toast every morning, always switches the vacuum cleaner on back to front and blows all the dust over my dinner.

DAD

Man who sometimes comes to our house when he ain't down the pub, shouting, "Where's my flamin' dinner, gal?" And snores so loudly my mum makes him sleep with Plasticine stuck up his nose.

KERRY PRESSWOOD

Girl who's nine and should be the first girl in space so she can't keep chasing me. But first, they've got to build a rocket big enough to carry her seeing as she is a great whale.

PHILIP STOCKS

My best friend, who keeps saying, "Cor, Benny Benson, you're brilliant, ain't you?" every time I do something. It's because he can't do much, being as he lost his brains on a trip to Blackpool once.

FATHER CHRISTMAS

Someone who spends al year making useless presents to bring me on December 25th. Also comes to Lewis Department store and calls my brother Sniffer a useless whatsit for pulling his beard off.

DRACULA

Someone real horrible what drinks your blood and has got big teeth. I've seen him come out of 3a Acacia Avenue, Bletchley and catch a number 39 bus.

BEASTLY HUTCHINS

He's my Headmaster, isn't he? He tells us about History and things like Alfred the Great who was King and burnt his mum's spaghetti hoops, just before he got to go out and sink the Spanish Armada.

BAKED BEANS HINDS

He is our football teacher and got red hair so we calls him carrot top, don't we?

MS SPRUGGINS

She tries to teach us things like Maths and topics. Because of Philip and me she keeps wondering why she ever went into teaching.

SCHOOL

Place where you goes to get tortured.

MY COUSIN ANGELA

Person what finds everything disgusting even McDonald's nuggets.

CARETAKER

Person what lives near the school and hates children just because they flicks paint accidental over the school floor.

THE BENNY BENSON SUPERGANG

A fit fighting force what fights Draculas and spies for the Government.

The Tree That Sat Down
by Beverley Nichols
£2.99

Once upon a time ... Judy and her grandmother kept
the shop under the Old Willow Tree in the enchanted
forest, selling everything that the animals needed. But
then comes competition in the persons of Sam and his
old grandfather, who open the Shop in the Ford. Sam
hires Miss Smith, a witch aided by spitting toads, to
dispose of his rivals. But neither Sam nor Miss Smith
had reckoned on the magic of Mr Tortoise.

The Stream that Stood Still
by Beverley Nichols
£2.99

Judy's son and daughter, Jack and Jill, confront Miss
Smith and the evil Sam. Jack is captured, changed into a
minnow, and held to ransom in the mouth of a great
pike. Jill goes in search of him – but it is Mr and Mrs
Beaver who dream up the master rescue.

The Mountain of Magic
by Beverley Nichols
£2.99

Armed with Mrs Judy's Alphabet of Magic and a very
special compass, Jack and Jill begin their perilous
journey up the Mountain of Magic. Thanks to the help
they receive from the Imp of the Mountain and a
caterpillar, Miss Smith and Sam are finally defeated.

Beyond the Rolling River by Kate Andrew £2.75

Toby and his chameleon friend Hardly Visible are desperately trying to find Glimrod, the lost Tuning Fork which controls the weather. Most important of all, they have to find it before Slubblejum the Nethercat does – for whoever controls the weather rules the world!

The Prism Tree by Kate Andrew £2.75

Toby and Hardly Visible are determined to foil Slubblejum's terrible plot to cut down the Prism Tree, for without the Tree there would be no colour in the world. But Toby and his friend are prisoners on the nethercat's ship. Can they escape in time?

Black Harvest by Ann Pilling £2.75

The ruggest west coast of Ireland seems like the perfect place for a holiday. Then everything starts to go wrong. Prill's dreams are haunted by a starv-ing woman; Baby Alison falls sick with a strange illness; Colin is aware of an awful smell. Only Oliver, their cousin remains unnervingly calm...

The Witch of Lagg by Ann Pilling £2.25

The ancient castle of Lagg hides a secret, though it's nothing as straightforward as a vampire. It's something with a very strange power. As Colin, Prill and Oliver explore the rambling old house and the dark woods surrounding it, they find themselves becoming the victims of some evil force, something full of threat...

The Fairy Rebel by Lynne Reid Banks

Jan is moping in the garden when Tiki is accidentally
"earthed" on her big toe. Being "earthed" for a fairy
means that she can be seen, and Tiki has just broken -
one of the most important fairy rules. Another
important rule is never to give humans magic favours,
but when Tiki hears Jan's very special wish, she is
determined to help, risking the Fairy Queen's fury with
frightening results.

The Farthest-Away Mountain
by Lynne Reid Banks

From Dakin's bedroom window, the farthest-away
mountain looks quite close. She can see the peak with
its multi-coloured snow clearly, just beyond the pine
wood. No one can tell her why the snow isn't white,
because no one has ever been there; for though the
mountain looks close, however far you travel it never
gets any closer. Then one morning, Dakin is woken by
a voice calling, summoning her to fight the evil on the
mountain and set it free...

I, Houdini by Lynne Reid Banks

Houdini is no ordinary hamster. Like his namesake, he
was born with quite exceptional talents for getting out
of cages. He chews, wriggles or squeezes his way out
of every cage his adoring people try to confine him to,
strewing chaos, havoc and flood behind him and
surviving fearful dangers.

All at £2.00

Vlad the Drac by Ann Jungman
£2.99
Paul and Judy are fed up with their holiday in Romania, until they find a baby vampire under a stone. They smuggle him into England, disguised as a souvenir, but all too soon the trouble starts.

Vlad the Drac Returns by Ann Jungman
£2.99
Vlad is on holiday in England, and he's bored. And whatever he starts out to do, poor old Vlad always ends up in a scrape – like the day he fell into a food mixer! Luckily Paul and Judy pick up the pieces.

Vlad the Drac Superstar by Ann Jungman
£2.99
Vlad comes to live with the Stones while he's starring in his first movie. Not only does he disrupt the whole film studio, but he becomes monstrously big for his boots at home.

Vlad the Drac Vampire by Ann Jungman
£2.99
As soon as Vlad hears about Paul and Judy's new baby sister, he comes to "help". To keep him out of mischief, Mum suggests that the children take him sightseeing – with disastrous, hilarious consequ-ences.

Vlad the Drac Down Under by Ann Jungman
£2.99
Vlad is appalled when he discovers he's on a plane to Australia with the Stone family – one trip to the beach is enough for a vampire who's more used to snow-clad mountains! But his feelings soon change.

Wagstaffe the Wind-Up Boy by Jan Needle
£3.50
Wagstaffe is so awful that his mother and father run away from home. Wagstaffe celebrates by playing a practical joke on a lorry on the M62 – a stupid thing to do: he's squashed flat. A brilliant doctor patches him up so he can undertake some great adventures.

Dakota of the White Flats by Philip Ridley
£2.75
Is there a monster hidden in old Medusa's carefully guarded supermarket trolley? Ten-year-old Dakota Pink cannot resist having a look, and before she knows it she is sailing towards an impenetrable fortress along a river full of killer eels.

Mercedes Ice by Philip Ridley
£1.95
In Shadow Point, a menacing and crumbling tower block, Hickory plays at being Queen of the basement with a cloak of cobweb. Her friend Mercedes is a prince, but he longs for his kingdom to be more colourful.

The Sword in the Stone by T. H. White
£3.99
The story of the enchanted (and enchanting) lessons which the boy nicknamed The Wart learns through his tutor, Merlyn the magician. This richly comic fantasy of King Arthur's times will appeal to all readers.

Hairline Cracks by Andrew Taylor
£2.99
Unwashed plates and a coffee cup on the floor: that's
how it all began. Sam knows there's something wrong
– his mother's cooked a meal and then disappeared.
He's willing to bet it's something she's discovered
about the local nuclear power station.

Snapshot by Andrew Taylor
£2.99
Chris meets the girl called Smith for the first time – and
gets involved in a deadly game of cat and mouse with
criminals who've already killed once to get what they
want. Now they want Smith... and Chris is the only
one who can stop them.

Double Exposure by Andrew Taylor
£2.99
Chris realises there's something very strange going on
at Smith's holiday cottage, but Smith herself is too
taken up with her father's new girlfriend to notice.
Then a ghostly face appears at a window, and shatters
what peace they had...

Negative Image by Andrew Taylor
£2.99
Chris was expecting a quiet weekend with Smith, but it
turns out there's a lot more to his visit than picnics on
the beach and country walks – and then he's kidnapped.
He knows they've got the wrong person, but how
much would his life be worth if he told them the truth?

Order Form

To order direct from the publishers, just make a list of the titles you want and fill in the form below:

Name ....

Address ....

....

....

....

Send to: Dept 6, HarperCollins Publishers Ltd, Westerhill Road, Bishopbriggs, Glasgow G64 2QT.

Please enclose a cheque or postal order to the value of the cover price, plus:

UK & BFPO: Add £1.00 for the first book, and 25p per copy for each addition book ordered.

Overseas and Eire: Add £2.95 service charge. Books will be sent by surface mail but quotes for airmail despatch will be given on request.

A 24-hour telephone ordering service is avail-able to Visa and Access card holders: 041-772 2281